... and He looked down at me and He said ...

That Old Chestnut...

by Sally Ann Lasson

...'this *is* a break!'

Bernard - doesn't think there's many problems that couldn't be solved with a good bottle of claret.

Liz - singularly objective character esp. about Bernard to whom, at time of going to press, she is married.

Shirley - single and confused. She goes out with Trevor but can't remember why.

Trevor - a bit of a dark horse. He is a man of few words, none of them are very interesting.

Index

Marriage

I don't know why people make such a
fuss about marriage and monogamy.
It's easy.. and I should know
I've done it four times.

Liz, we've got so much going for us
let's start afresh and really make a go of it.
Bernard, the only thing we've got in common
is that we got married on the same day.

If I had my life to live over again, I don't think I'd bother
Oh, cheer up Shirl. You're better off without him. He'd only get in the way
In the way of what?
Other men. Look, you've got to see this as a learning experience, an opportunity to get out there and be something.
But there's nothing I want to be
There must be something. Think about it
Well, there is one thing.
What?
Married.

Where are there any decent men?
God knows. I'm just making do with Shorty for now
Oh yeah. He's the one who doesn't know who Nietzsche is
but he does know where Katharine Hamnett is
That's the one. I did once meet a handsome intelligent totally fab guy
And what happened?
Oh, it didn't work out
Why not?
I married him.

I wonder what they're like, you know, when they're alone.
Oh, I think they get on quite well...
for married people.
yes, but it seems more like a business arrangement than anything else.
Do you know what his idea of foreplay is?
No.
Lift your nightie.
So they married for love then.
yeah. Love of money.

Don't dwell on past failures - move on to new ones

BERNARD!!! COME HERE!
Oh God, not another argument please.
I can still remember the last time I got my own way
marriage is not a competition Bernard
AND THIS IS NOT AN ARGUMENT
This is a discussion and what I'd like to know is this.
why do you always come home so late?
Oh, that's easy.
Because I've got nowhere else to go.

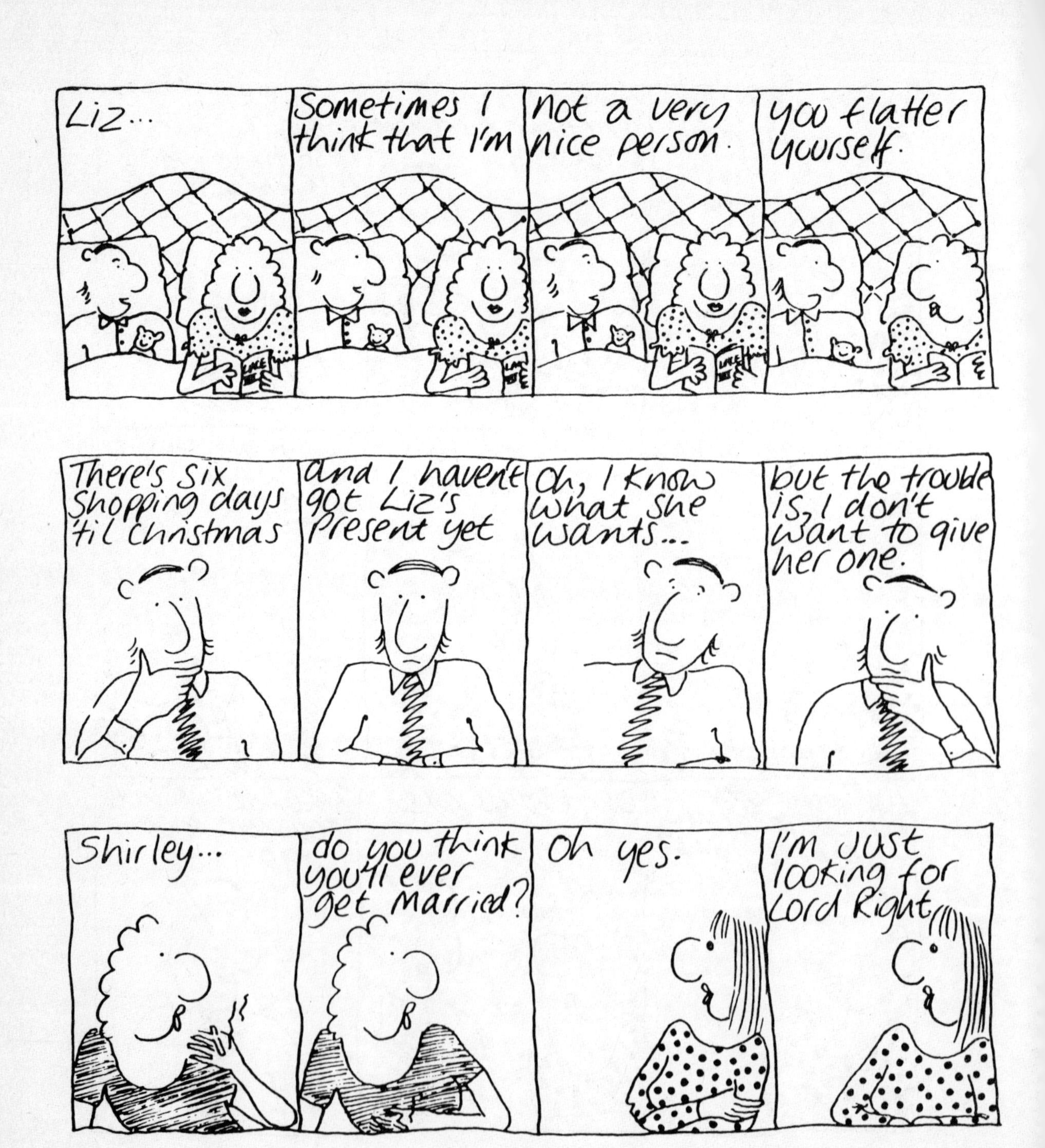
Liz...
Sometimes I think that I'm
not a very nice person.
you flatter yourself.
There's six shopping days 'til christmas
and I haven't got Liz's present yet
Oh, I know what she wants...
but the trouble is, I don't want to give her one.
Shirley...
do you think you'll ever get married?
Oh yes.
I'm just looking for Lord Right.

BERNARD! That bloody woman phoned again
What, Mother?
Yes. God I loathe her
I hate the way she fusses over you as if you were a baby
... the Messiah perhaps.
Your mother ruined you Bernard
She did every-thing for you
She even paid your friends to play with you.
She made you what you aren't today.

Trevor, I want my freedom
I love you but I need to find myself
Really get to know myself
Be a free spirit
I feel bogged down
We've been together for 3 years now
and I feel the wind of change blowing.
I'm leaving you.
Unless you marry me.

Domestic Bliss or Breaking up is NOT hard to do

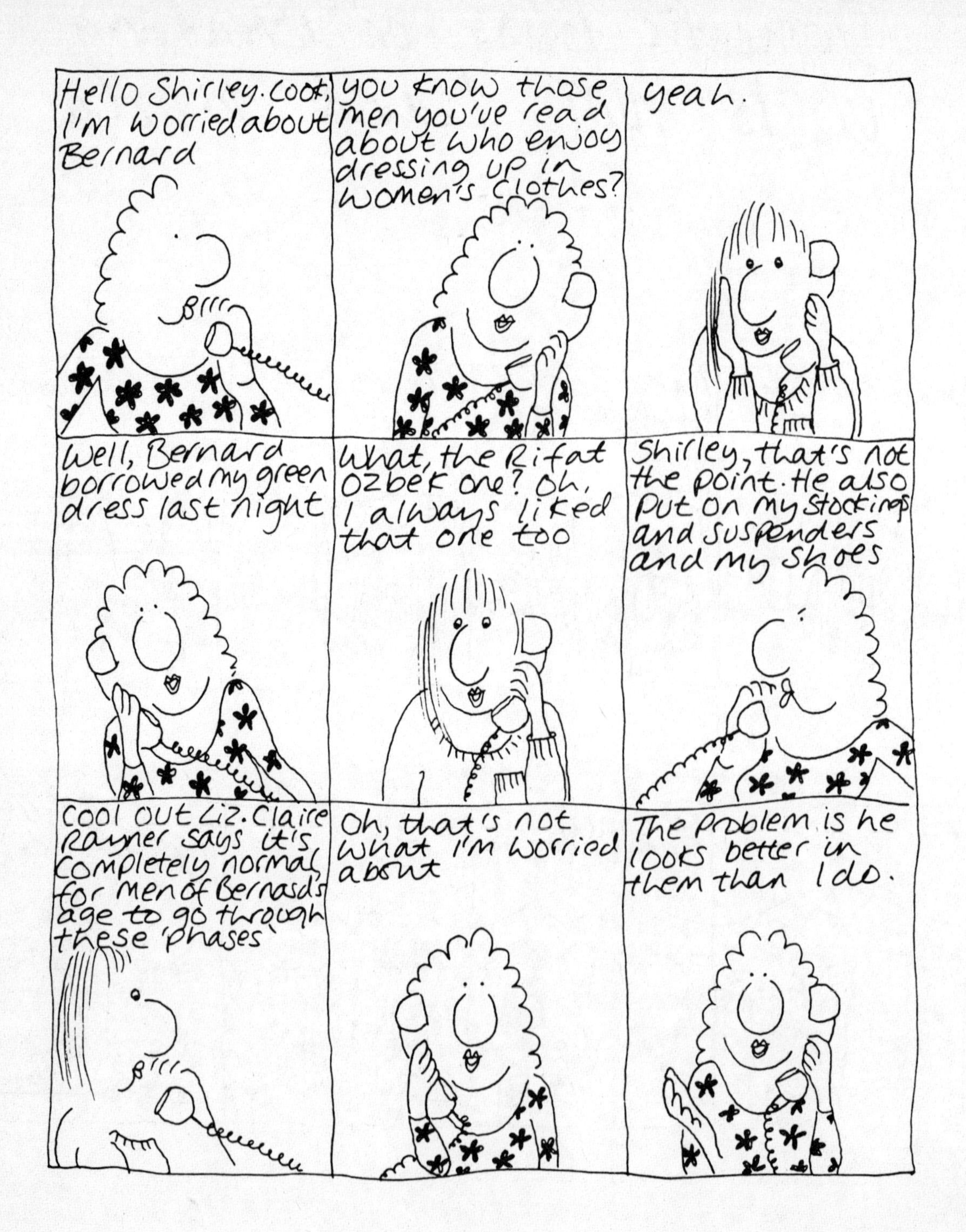
Hello Shirley. Coot, I'm worried about Bernard
you know those men you've read about who enjoy dressing up in women's clothes?
yeah.
Well, Bernard borrowed my green dress last night
What, the Rifat Ozbek one? Oh, I always liked that one too
Shirley, that's not the point. He also put on my stockings and suspenders and my shoes
Cool out Liz. Claire Rayner says it's completely normal for men of Bernard's age to go through these 'phases'
Oh, that's not what I'm worried about
The problem is he looks better in them than I do.

Where there's a will there's a relative

Bernard...
Will you still love me when I'm old?
Oh yes.
So long as you look 18.

Divorce isn't the end of the world...
...but you can see it from there.

She's gone to see her lawyer about her divorce settlement
but she says she'll call you later.
How long will she be?
Don't know. How long does it take to get blood out of a stone?

Liz, sometimes you drive me so crazy
I think that if you were a man, I'd kill you.
Oh, don't worry Bernard. If I were a man
I'd kill myself.

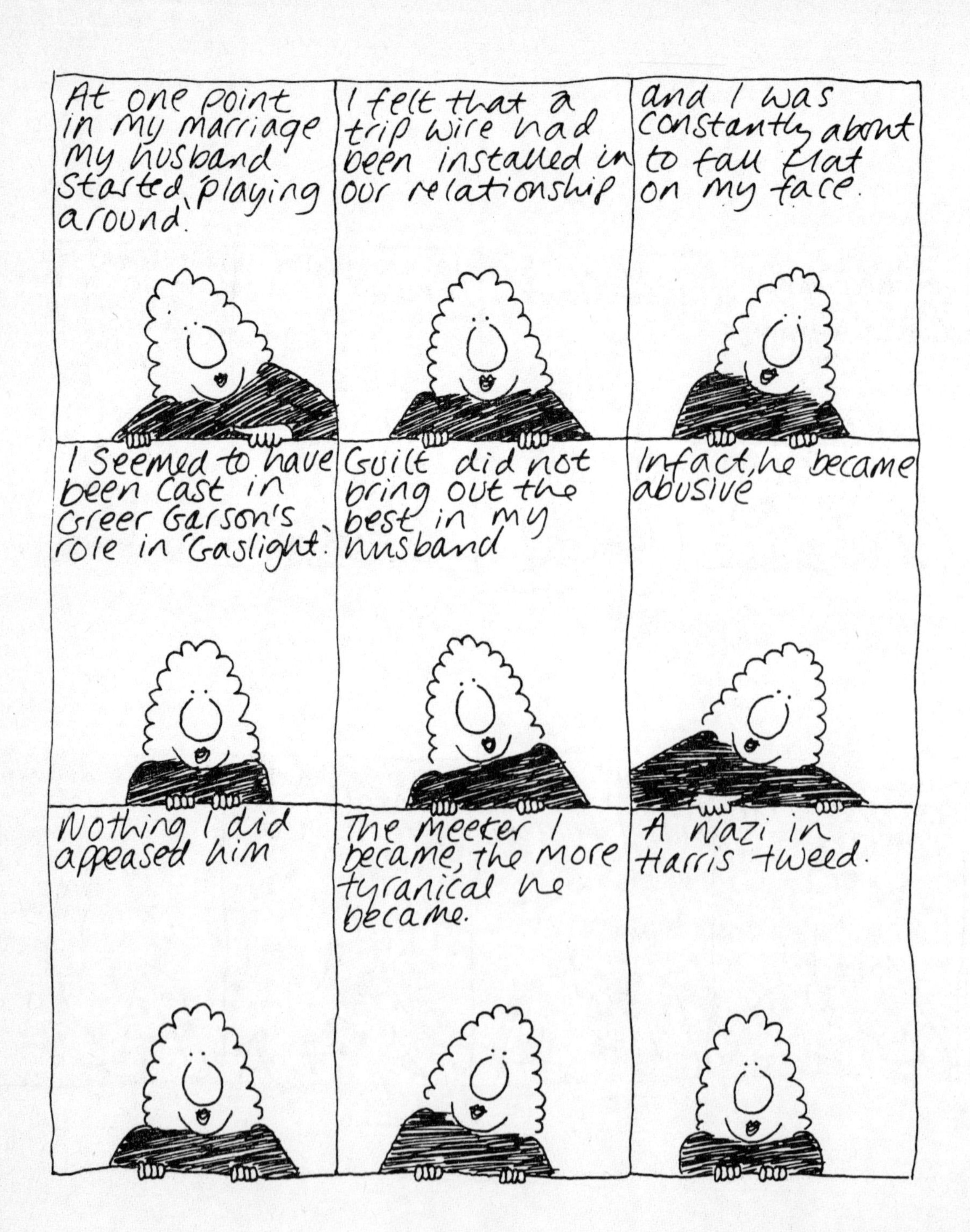
At one point in my marriage my husband started 'playing around'.
I felt that a trip wire had been installed in our relationship
and I was constantly about to fall flat on my face.
I seemed to have been cast in Greer Garson's role in 'Gaslight'.
Guilt did not bring out the best in my husband
Infact, he became abusive
Nothing I did appeased him
The meeker I became, the more tyranical he became.
A Nazi in Harris tweed.

I was just reading this lovely story
about this couple who fall in love
in the Austrian alps
and have passionate encounters in pastures
covered in edelweiss.
So what happened in the end?
Oh, it had a happy ending.
They split up.

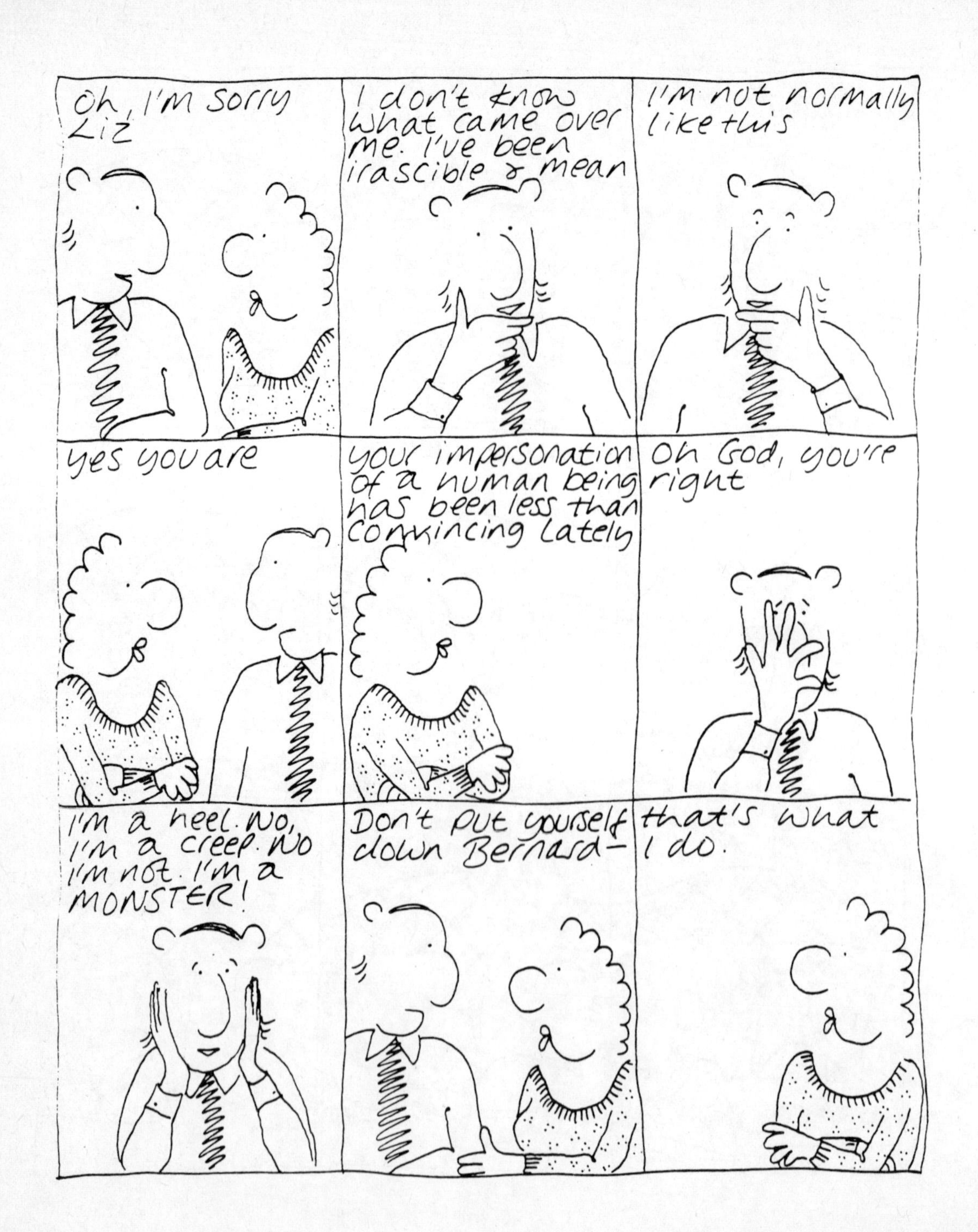
Oh, I'm sorry Liz
I don't know what came over me. I've been irascible & mean
I'm not normally like this
yes you are
your impersonation of a human being has been less than convincing lately
Oh God, you're right
I'm a heel. No, I'm a creep. No I'm not. I'm a MONSTER!
Don't put yourself down Bernard-
that's what I do.

Infidelity

So what is it?
What's she got that I haven't?
Is she prettier than me?
Liz, **I'm** prettier than you.

It's funny, but when a woman commits adultery she says
"I'm sorry, there must be something the matter with me"
And when a man commits adultery he says
"I'm sorry, there must be something the matter with **YOU**."

And I could tell he was lying.
Oh, that's alright then
If a man bothers to lie to you
you know he cares.

I'm depressed. I've been going through Bernard's credit card statement
and there's all these petrol station payments listed.
Well, what's wrong with that?
He doesn't drive.

My boyfriend still won't commit himself
So when he went away on business last week
I spent the night with an ex-lover of mine
And what's he like?
Gorgeous, sexy and rich
Well he sounds like a better prospect. Why don't you go for him instead?
Oh, it would never work
Why not?
Because he's incapable of being faithful.

Hello Shirley. I've got herpes
What?
My husband doesn't believe me
Doesn't believe you?
He doesn't believe I caught it off a loo seat
A loo seat?
Yeah, a loo seat.
What loo seat?
My boyfriend's.

Bernard's gone away on a business trip
Oh yeah.
yeah. And I found a packet of condoms in his suitcase
My God.
That's what I said
And he said he didn't intend using them
So?
So I said you must do or you wouldn't have bought them
And he said in that case World War III would've happened by now.

I know I've committed adultery
and that's wrong. But the funny thing is
I don't feel in the least bit guilty about it.
That's because you didn't enjoy it enough.

Why does a man commit adultery?
Why does a dog lick his balls?
Dunno. Why?
Because he can.

I've met this lovely man
You haven't?
Yeah, he's really sexy and he wants my body
He doesn't?
Yeah, and I'm going to give it to him
But what about Bernard?
What about Bernard?
Well, imagine how you'll feel afterwards
Mmm.

Liz,
I'm in a bit of a conundrum.
Oh yeah.
I'm trying to work my life out
to some sort of simple conclusion
but I'm confused about the whole sex thing
I don't know what it is about monogamy
that makes it so difficult.
I do.

Sex

Mmm...
Wow Michael...
that was really amazing.
Hey, don't tell me – tell your friends.

What's the most important thing that happened to you this week:
a) The Eurovision Song Contest (b) The General Election announcement or (c) Bernard making love to you?
Bernard's making love to me, of course.
Eurovision happens every year and the election happens every four.

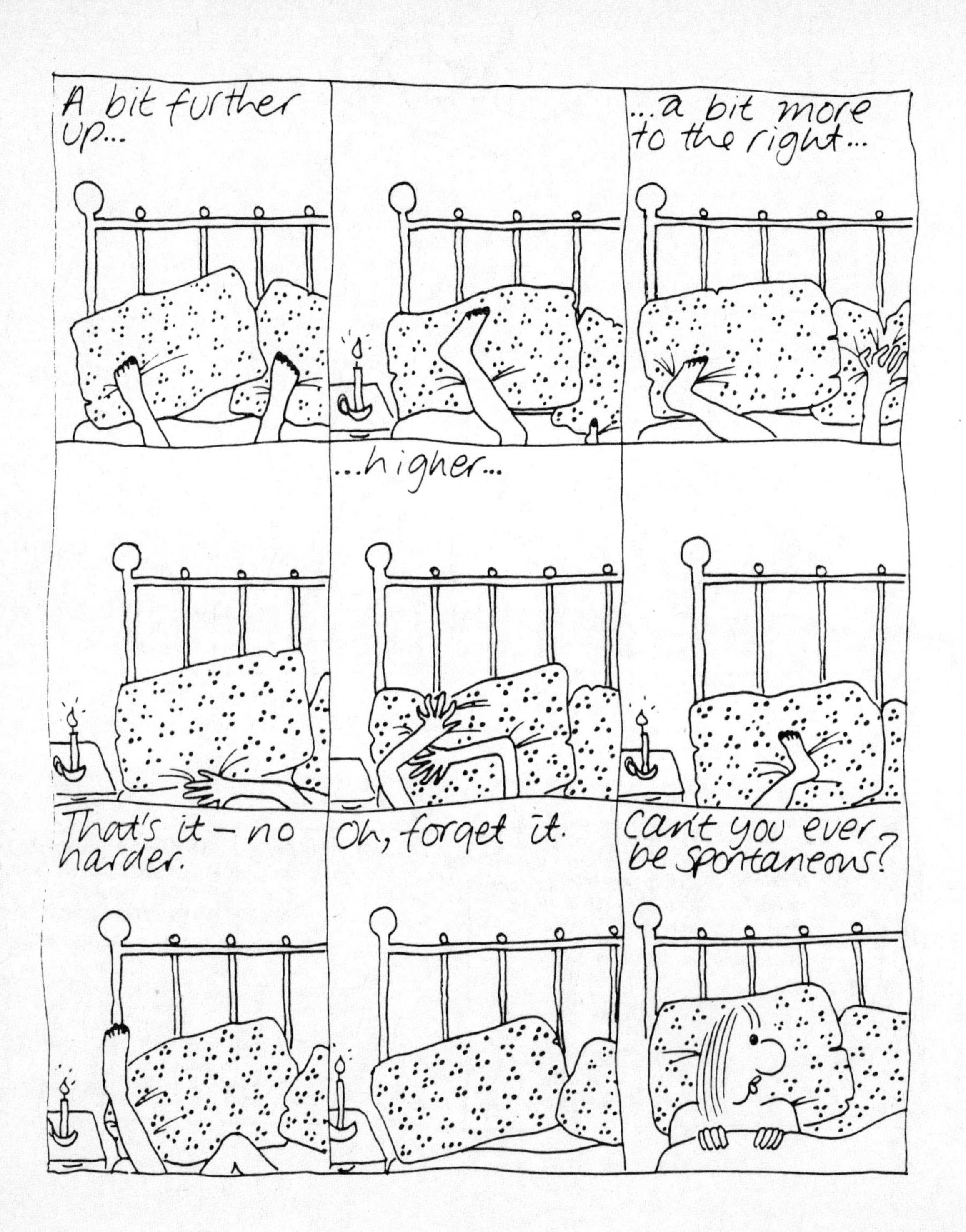
A bit further up...
...a bit more to the right...
...higher...
That's it — no harder.
Oh, forget it.
Can't you ever be spontaneous?

Liz...
I want your body,
Well you can't have it
I haven't finished with it yet

Bernard...
make love to me.
Do it yourself.

I was just reading this article about AIDS
XENO
and I've been having a think.
XENO
Oh God.
There ought to be a law against it.
I mean, if you sleep with someone and you know you've got AIDS
then it's murder.
Isn't it?
I suppose so. But then,
I've always felt sex was murder.

I caught Bernard under the mistletoe with Sarah-Jane again.
But she's so thick what do they talk about in the gaps between doing it?
God knows.
And if I know Bernard they'll be awfully long gaps.

I was just reading this Home Office report on what duties an au-pair has.
It says you shouldn't ask an au-pair to do anything you wouldn't do yourself.
Like what?
Well... like sleeping with Bernard.

I don't understand why anyone like Jeffrey Archer
would spend money on a tart.
After all...
he could've spent it on himself.

So how's your sex life then?
Oh tolerable. Bernard's trying. Very trying.
Personally, I've always thought that when women say
they don't mind what size a man is, they're lying.
Oh I agree.
So what do you do then. Lie back and think of England?
NO, Ethiopia.
Why Ethiopia?
Because it's small and under developed.

Was it good for you too Shirley?
It was lovely.
No, but was it really good?
It was really really super.
But was it the best ever?
Z
Z
Z

Boys

Hello Liz. I've been chucked again.
So what went wrong this time?
One of two things. (A) He didn't know how much I cared.
Or (B) He did know how much I cared.

Boys... yuck.
They're all after one thing
and the trouble is...
it's never the same thing.

The smaller the man, the bigger the gift

So what were these manifold gifts you gave him?
A cassette of L'Après Midi d'un faun
An etching of his house, hand coloured
And a lilac T-shirt.
Anything else?
Oh yes.
And my heart, body and soul.
And what did he give you?
A throat infection.

Do you think you talked to that girl for long enough?
What girl?
That fat girl you talked to all evening
Oh her. We were just talking about politics.
She was fat. Infact, she was huge.
She was interesting to talk to
How come you always talk to pretty girls?
I thought you said she was fat.
Not fat enough. Stop the car.

yes Mother
No Mother
Mmm
MOTHER! That's a revolting suggestion
He's never even hinted at doing anything like THAT.
Mmm
Mmm
But Mother, I am looking for Mr. Right
It's just that in the meantime anyone will do.

Patrick, I'm touched to know that you care
But it'll never work
You keep trying to understand women...
and I keep confusing you with information.

There are four men I care about at the moment
but the one I care most about is the one who cares least about me.
Do you think you're perverse?
No. I think he is.

What do you get when you kiss a guy
You get enough germs to catch pneumonia
Then afterwards he'll never phone you...
Oh, sod it. Hello, is Pablo there?

What's up with Bernard?
Oh, he's having a second childhood.
Well he doesn't look very happy about it.
He's not. He didn't enjoy the first one.

Love...
Can make fools out of men
But can it make men
out of fools?

So after 40 minutes of this man soliloquizing I asked him "Now that I know where you
live, what you do, which school you went to, and the fact that you prefer dogs to cats,
is there anything at all about me that you'd like to know?"
And he said "No, not really."

DEALING WITH BOYS PART 1: Punctuality
I think...
you're...
late!
BLAM

Gosh Liz,
you know it must be nice to be rich and stupid.
Well, don't worry Bernard
you're half way there.

Life

Now that we're fully evolved human beings
who can role with the punches
and are mature enough to deal with life with a sense of humour
the problem is what do we do with what we know?

I've worked it out! I know the meaning of life!
The meaning of life is...
er... now what was it? ... um... no...
Sorry. It's gone again.

Don't smash the rich – go and stay with them

I've had the bathroom Marbleised
the drawing room stippled
and the hall-way ragged.
Now what am I going to do about me?

I can't go on. I'm sick with nerves and my headaches continually.
I feel like I've been violated and I'm wandering down a Kafka tunnel
What's wrong?
The builders started this morning.

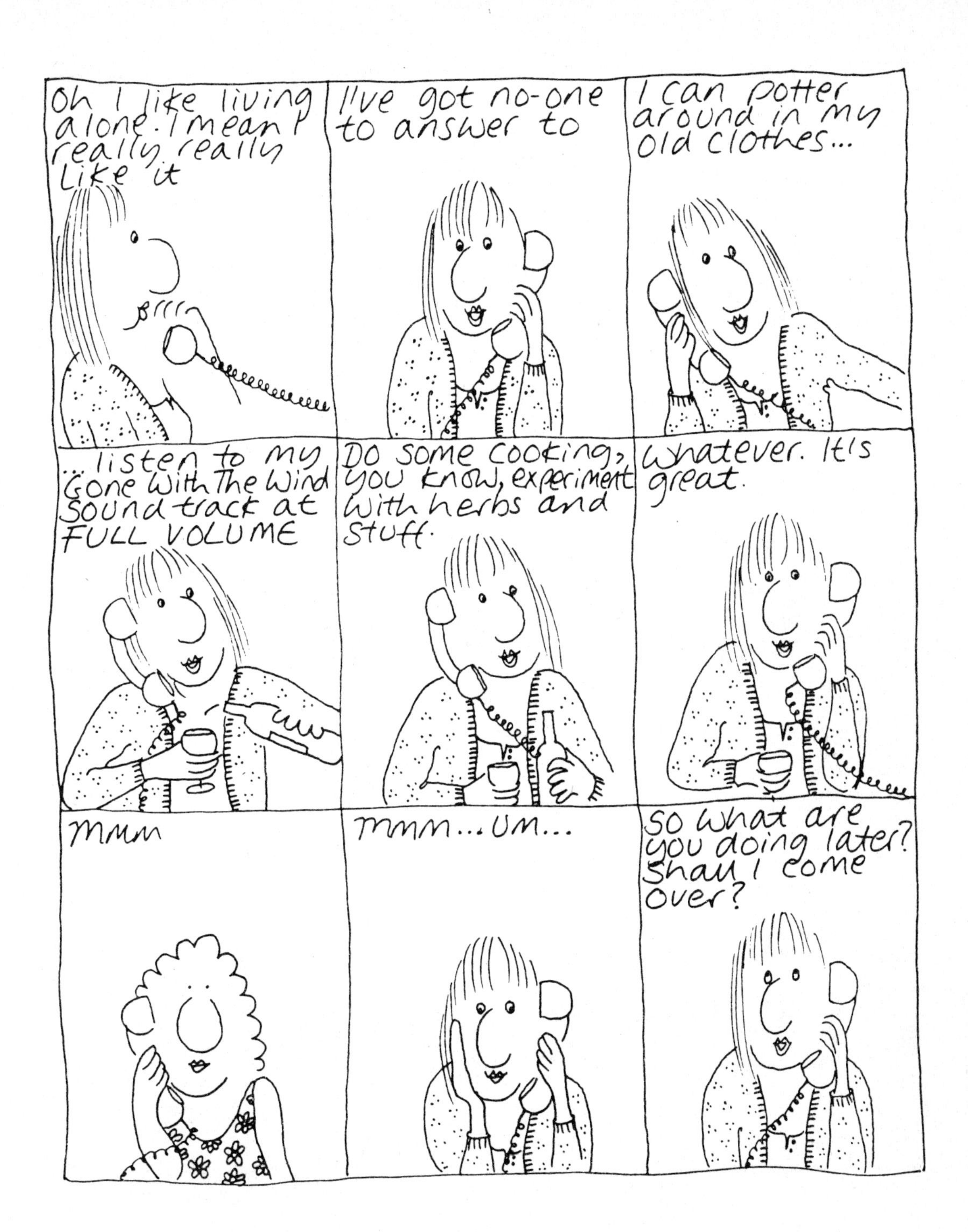
Oh I like living alone. I mean I really really like it
brrrr
I've got no-one to answer to
I can potter around in my old clothes...
...listen to my Gone With The Wind Sound track at FULL VOLUME
Do some cooking, you know, experiment with herbs and stuff.
Whatever. It's great.
mmm
mmm...um...
So what are you doing later? Shall I come over?

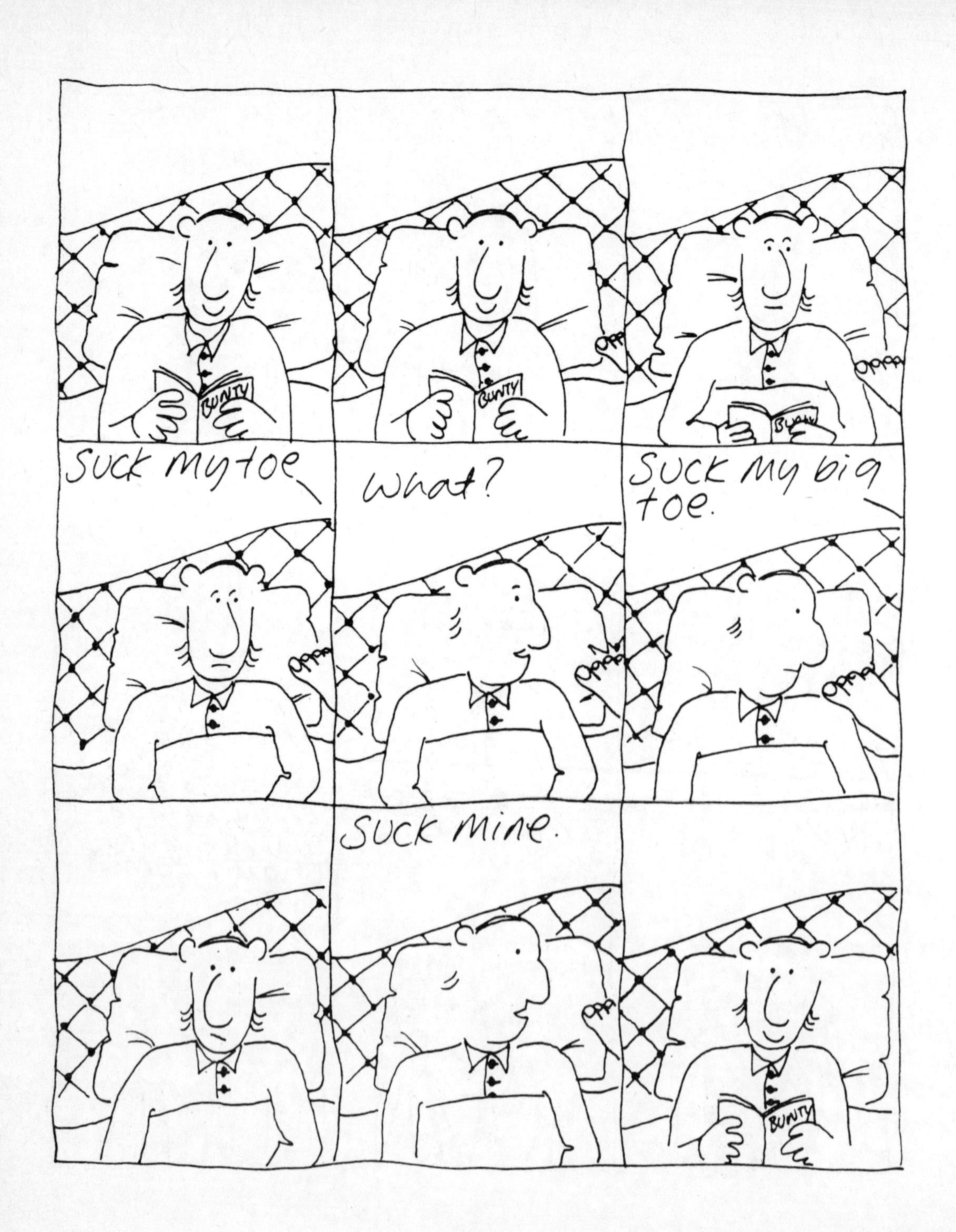
BUNTY
BUNTY
BUNTY
SUCK my toe
What?
SUCK my big toe.
SUCK mine.
BUNTY

The trouble is, you're born knowing you only have 70 yrs to live
So you waste most of it wondering how to Make the most of it.
And then what happens?
you die.

And then, without warning, he just walked out
and she never saw him again
Wow. It's a funny thing life.
yes, but compared to what?

Better a bad personality than none at all

Oh dear...
I seem to have lost my early spontaneity
But I'm working on it.

So I looked up at God
and I said 'God, give me a break'
and He looked down at me and He said
'This is a break.'

So what happened to her?
Well, she attacked THE MEANING OF LIFE with a vengeance
And in the end she knew all of the answers
But by then she'd forgotten the question.

four thousand eight hundred and twenty-four
four thousand eight hundred and twenty-five
Bernard. You can't take it with you.
Well, in that case... I'm not going.

How old is she?
Well, she's either a very well preserved older person
Or a very badly preserved younger person
Oh, you mean she's 40.

Whinge whinge whinge.
moan moan moan.
feminism's just
designer nagging.

Have you ever felt bored and depressed
and so fat that all you want to do is eat,
and sleep
and watch T.V.
As though there's no excitement in life
but you're too cowardly to end it all?
All the time.
So?
So?

Mountaineering!
Mountaineering?
yeah, it must be so exciting
Climbing thousands of feet up
Where man's never been
conquering ones own fears.
like Prince Charles says.
Isn't it dangerous?
Only if you fall off.

AIDS
AIDS
AIDS
DON'T DIE
AIDS!
LATEST!
AIDS
I'm sick to death of it.

I saw P.C. Coleman last night
Trouble is, they all look the same.
What, blacks?
No, policemen.

Shirley, stop making excuses
and get on with your life.
This is not a dress rehersal...
THIS IS IT.

Vices

Uncle Bernard,
show me your trick.
What trick?
Well aunty Liz says you can drink like a fish.

Bernard...
Do you think you've got a drink problem?
No... well
Only when I can't have one.

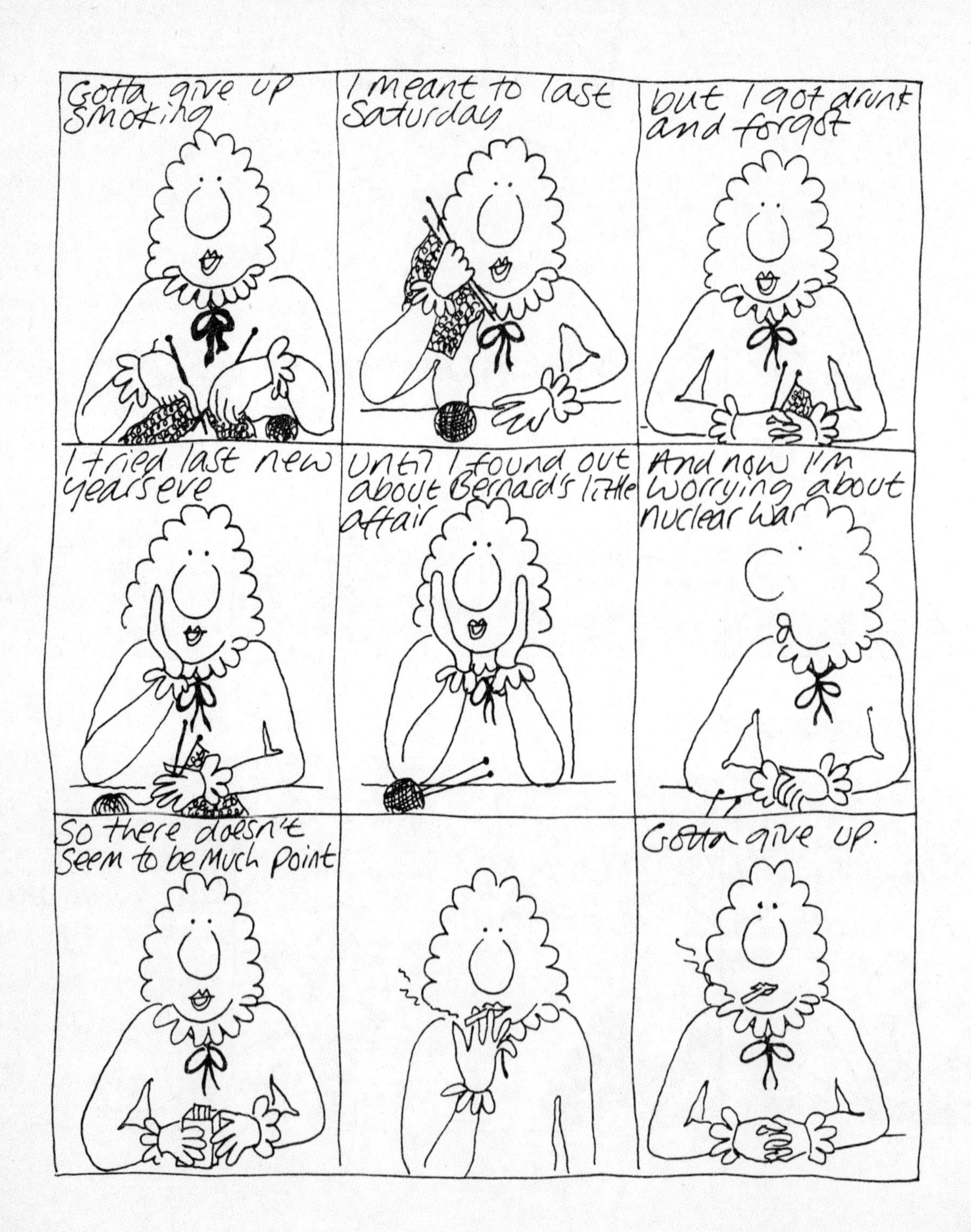
Gotta give up Smoking
I meant to last Saturday
but I got drunk and forgot
I tried last new years eve
Until I found out about Bernard's little affair
And now I'm worrying about nuclear war
So there doesn't seem to be much point
Gotta give up.

What do you think of this little wine Trevor?
It's delicious Bernard.
I think it's very tasty Bernard.
It's a full-bodied wine from the northern Bordeaux region...
to be precise, a small Chateau called du Bosquet...
where they just have the 100 acres...
but use the Cabernat franc grape to its best advantage.
Bernard, there's something about the way you talk about wine...
that makes me want to drink so much of it.

Bernard...
are you drunk?
NO. Dean martin says you're not drunk if you can
lie on the floor without holding on.

Bernard, Putting articles about lung cancer under my pillow
isn't going to make me stop smoking.
Oh well. Every-one gives up...
eventually.

Liz, have you noticed how few people smoke today
yeah. I hate being made to feel like a leper.
I know, it's getting really bad.
we're part of a dying breed.

British Library Cataloguing in Publication Data
Lasson, Sally Ann
That old chestnut.
I. Title
828'.91407

ISBN 0-450-49527-2

First published in Great Britain 1989

Published by New English Library,
a hardcover imprint of Hodder and Stoughton,
a division of Hodder and Stoughton Ltd,
Mill Road, Dunton Green, Sevenoaks, Kent TN13 2YA
Editorial Office: 47 Bedford Square, London WC1B 3DP

Printed in Great Britain by
St Edmundsbury Press Ltd, Bury St Edmunds, Suffolk.